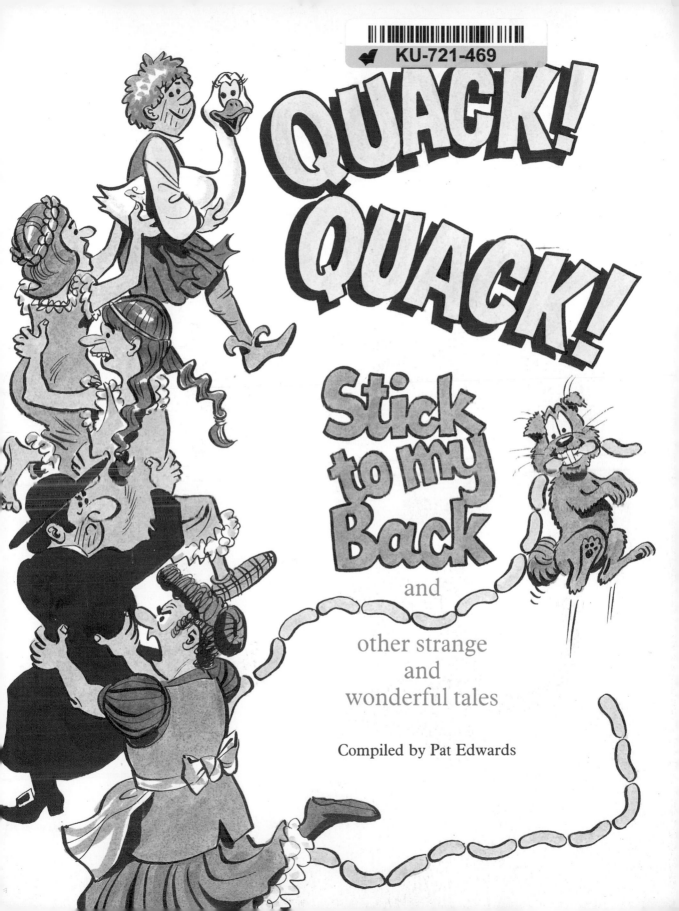

QUACK! QUACK!

Stick to my Back

and

other strange
and
wonderful tales

Compiled by Pat Edwards

Acknowledgements

We are grateful to the following for permission to reproduce copyright material: William Heinemann Ltd for the story 'Puss in Boots' by Paul Galdone; Longman Group UK Ltd for the story 'The Princess and The Pea' retold by Milton Subotsky in *The Golden Treasury of Classic Fairy Tales* (pub. Longman Group UK Ltd 1983); Penguin Books Ltd for the poem 'Catnap' from *Songs For My Dog and Other People* by Max Fatchen (Kestrel Books 1980) Copyright © 1980 by Max Fatchen; Penguin Books Australia Ltd for the poem 'Thank You Dad For Everything' from *The Fed Up Family Album* by Doug Macleod (pub. Penguin Books Australia Ltd); Ward Lock Educational Co. Ltd for the story 'Tom and The Ghost' in *Short Tales 3* by Geoffrey Summerfield. Illustrations to 'Puss in Boots' by permission of William Heinemann Ltd; illustrations to 'The Princess and The Pea' by permission of Ian Moo-Young © Moo Movies Productions Ltd.

Illustrators, other than those acknowledged with each story, include: Steve Biesty pp.40–41; Wendy Elks p.39; Ian Forss pp.26–27; Linda Forss pp.14–15, 64; Peter Foster pp.4–13; Paul Galdone pp.45–62; Geoff Hocking pp.16–21; Craig Smith pp.42–43; Allan Stomann pp.24–25; Sylvia Witte pp.44, 63; David Woodward pp.22–23.

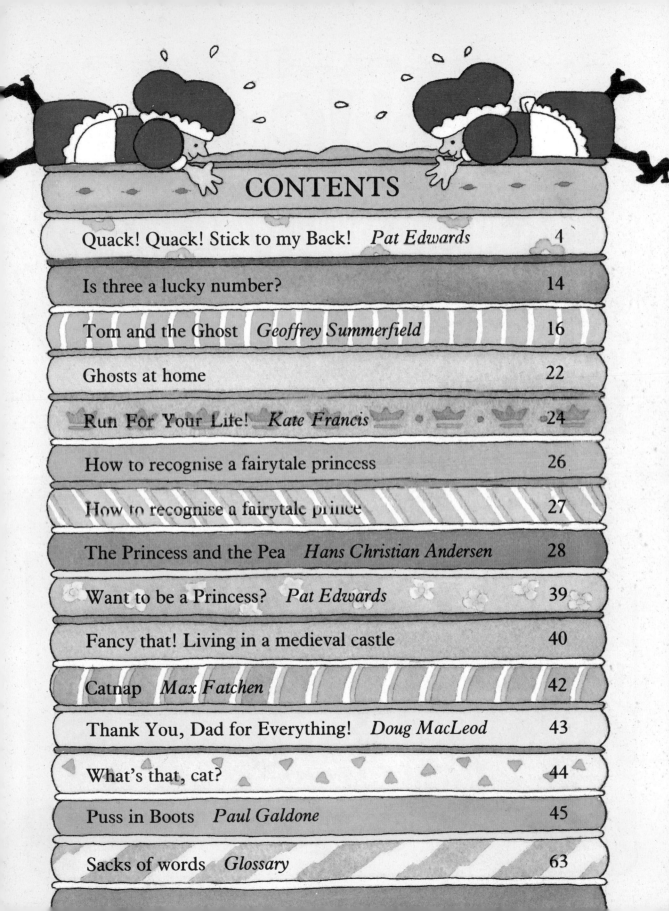

CONTENTS

Quack! Quack! Stick to my back!

Italian Folktale retold by *Pat Edwards*; illustrated by *Peter Foster*.

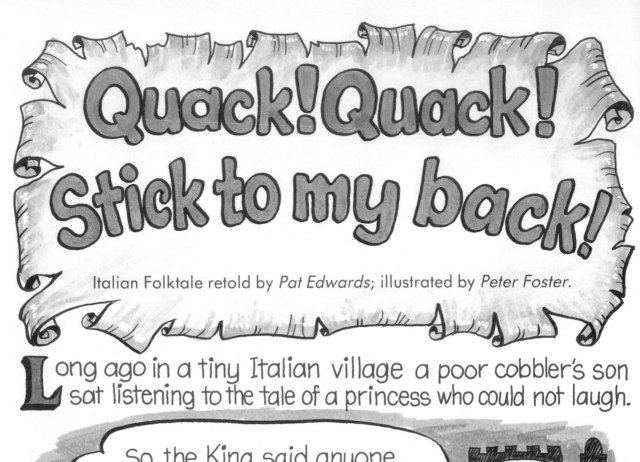

Long ago in a tiny Italian village a poor cobbler's son sat listening to the tale of a princess who could not laugh.

So the King said anyone who could make the Princess laugh, could **marry** her.

Why shouldn't I try?

But Sandrino would not listen to his poor old father.

Along the road to town Sandrino met a poor old woman.

Could you give me something to eat, young man? I am very hungry!

Sure. Take this.

And kind-hearted Sandrino gave her all three of his loaves.

Thank you, Thank you.

Don't mention it!

On and on he went until he met another poor old woman.

Could you give me some money to buy a dress, young man? I'm very cold.

CHATTER

CHATTER

Sure. Take this.

6

And kind-hearted Sandrino gave her all three of his gold coins.

Thank you, Thank you.

Don't mention it!

But further along the road he met a third poor old woman.

Could you give me something to drink, young man? I am very thirsty.

Sure. Take this!

As soon as she'd drunk the bottle of wine, the old woman turned into a beautiful maiden.

I know you are kind-hearted because I am the three old women.

PLF!

WOW!

I'm going to help you. Take this goose and carry it with you everywhere you go.

Everywhere?

When anyone touches it, it will cry, "Quack, Quack!" and straight away you must say, "Stick to my back."

Okay!

At that, the beautiful maiden vanished leaving Sandrino alone with the goose.

So Sandrino and the goose went on towards the town. Near nightfall they came to an inn.

We'll have to sit out here all night, goose. I've no money to pay for a room.

GWK!

What a fine meal it would make!

Let's ask him in!

Look at that fine goose, Sister.

The wicked innkeeper and his daughters decided to steal the goose.

Here's a fine room for you— and it's free.

Let me take your goose out to the barn.

8

But Sandrino would not part with his goose.

No, thanks. We must stick together.

We'll steal it while he sleeps!

SNIGGER! SNORK!

foster

As they passed a church a priest looked out.

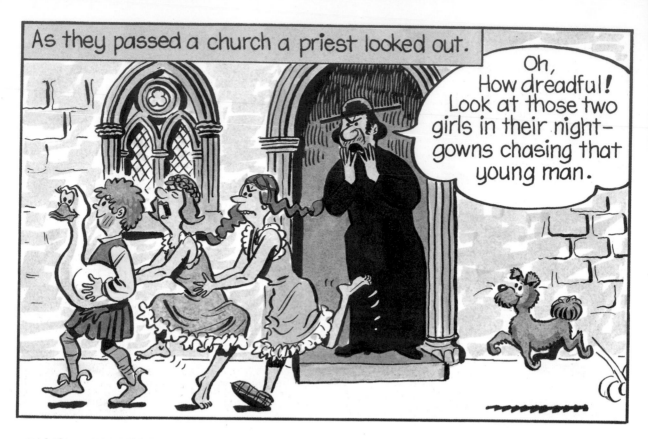

Oh, How dreadful! Look at those two girls in their nightgowns chasing that young man.

But as soon as he put his hands on the young girl...

Shame on you. Leave that young man alone.

QUACK! QUACK!

Stick to my back!

Let go of me!

And now there were three of them stuck to the goose.

Near the palace they met a sausage seller.

Oh! How dreadful! Look at that priest chasing after those two girls in their nightgowns!

SNF! SNF!

Shame on you! Leave those young girls alone.

?

Stick to my back!

Let go of me you rascal!

QUACK! QUACK!

Just then the princess came out on the balcony.

11

When the Princess saw the strange group she burst out laughing.

Quick! Tell the King the Princess is laughing.

Look, Father! See how funny they are!

When the King came he started laughing too.

Well, I made her laugh!

And while they laughed, the goose disappeared and everyone came unstuck.

Then the King sent for Sandrino.

You look pretty scruffy. How about being a servant instead of marrying the Princess?

No thanks! I want the Princess.

So they bathed him and dressed him in fine clothes and suddenly he looked like a prince.

How do I look?

My hero!

Wonderful, Prince Sandrino!

And the wedding feast was the finest anyone had ever seen.

We're going to live happily ever after!

King, meet my Dad!

How do, King?

Er, How do you do, Cobbler!

Is Three a Lucky Number?

Sandrino met three old women before he met the goose.

In stories, fairies always give three wishes.

So do I.

And the heroine or hero usually has three tasks to do to win the treasure or the princess.

The number three is used a lot in fairy stories and folk tales. No one knows why it became a lucky number. A long time ago, when people were superstitious and believed in magic, they thought that both good and bad things came in threes. Letters and visitors, they said, usually did and if you broke two things, then you'd be sure to break a third one. Is it true? Of course not!

Tom and The Ghost

Long, long ago an old house was haunted by a ghost. The ghost always haunted the same room, so nobody would sleep there. But it also made a lot of noise, banging and crashing about, so that the people of the house could never enjoy a good night's sleep.

Finally, they were so tired of being haunted, they sent for Tom, who was well known for getting rid of unwanted ghosts. The family gave him a good supper. Before they went off to bed, they gave Tom three things that he asked for: an empty bottle, a bottle of brandy, and a jug of water.

So Tom settled down for the night. He locked himself in the haunted room, and sat down to wait for the arrival of the ghost. For a couple of hours, Tom sat quietly, sipping his brandy and water, and then, as soon as the church bell sounded the chimes of midnight, there in front of Tom stood the ghost, as large as life.

"Well, Tom," said the ghost, "and how are you?"

"Oh, I can't grumble," said Tom. "But how did you know my name?"

"Oh, very well indeed," said the ghost.

17

Tom didn't think much of this answer but decided not to complain.

"But how did you manage to get into this room?" Tom asked.

"Oh, very easily."

Again, that wasn't much of an answer, but Tom didn't complain. Instead, he said, "Not through the door, I'll be bound."

"No, not through the door, but through the keyhole," said the ghost.

"That's a likely tale," said Tom, "I think you're pulling my leg."

"Oh, but I did come through the keyhole," said the ghost.

"Yes, and you can pull the other one," said Tom.

"But I did," said the ghost.

"But I'm sure you can't get through the keyhole," said Tom.

"And I'm sure I can," said the ghost.

"Well, if you can get through the keyhole,
you can get into this bottle," said Tom, pointing
to the empty bottle.

"Easy," said the ghost.

"I don't believe it," said Tom.

"It's true," said the ghost.

"I'll believe it when I see it," said Tom,
holding out the bottle.

"How's this, then?" said the ghost, and
slipped into the bottle.

"Very good," said Tom, popping a cork into

the mouth of the bottle.

So, there was the ghost, safe and sound, inside the bottle. Then Tom slipped downstairs, walked to the bridge where the river was wide and deep and threw the bottle into the deepest part of the river.

"And that's the last we'll see of you," said Tom.

And so it was.

by *Geoffrey Summerfield*, illustrated by *Geoff Hocking*   21

RUN FOR YOUR LIFE!

A computer story! *Kate Francis*

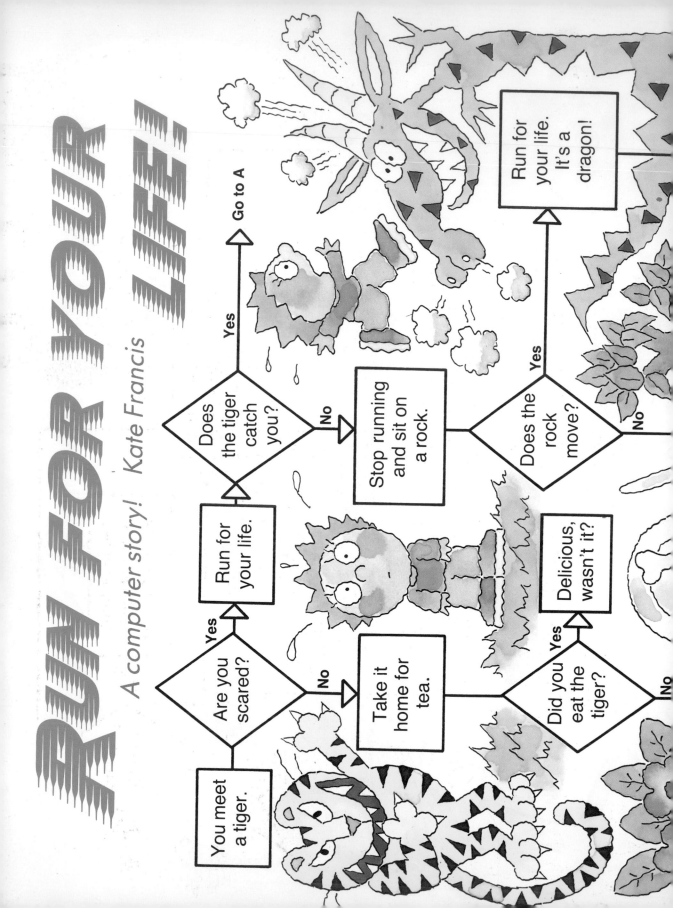

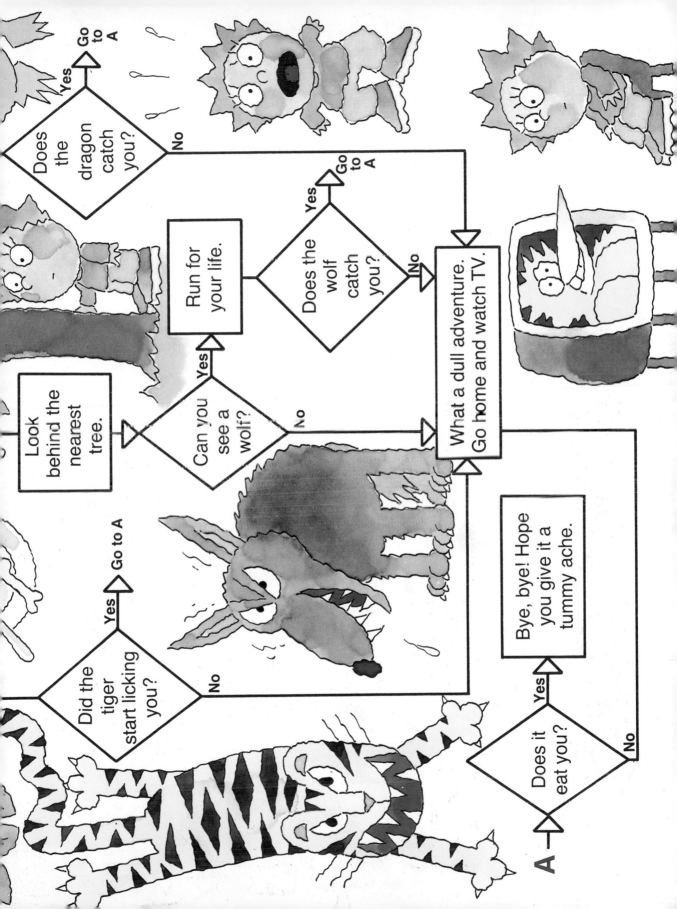

How to recognise a Fairytale Princess

1. She lives in a castle and sometimes has trouble laughing.
2. She often wears ridiculous slippers made of glass.
3. She's probably called Florinda or Ysolda instead of Jane or Molly.
4. She has trouble sleeping on peas, even when the bed has one hundred mattresses.
5. She never has red hair. It's always golden and long enough to make a ladder.
6. She has a fairy godmother instead of a proper grandmother.
7. She kisses frogs.

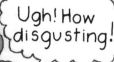

Ugh! How disgusting!

How to recognise a Fairytale Prince

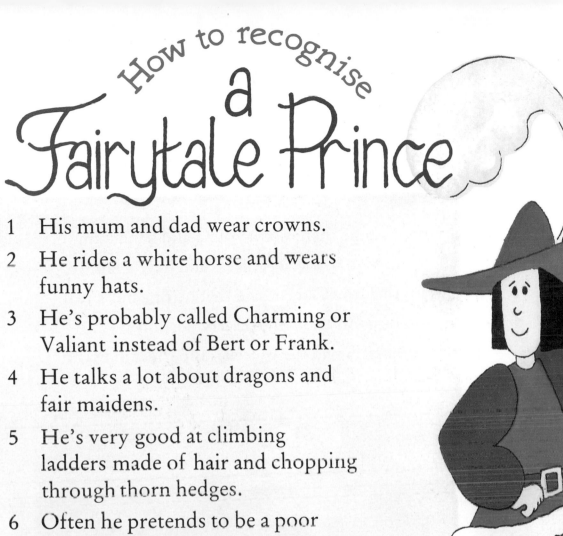

1   His mum and dad wear crowns.

2   He rides a white horse and wears funny hats.

3   He's probably called Charming or Valiant instead of Bert or Frank.

4   He talks a lot about dragons and fair maidens.

5   He's very good at climbing ladders made of hair and chopping through thorn hedges.

6   Often he pretends to be a poor woodcutter until after the girl has promised to marry him.

7   Sometimes he's a frog.

Ugh! How disgusting!

The princess and the pea

Once upon a time there was a young and handsome prince, who wanted to marry a princess and have a family.

But his mother, the Queen, said that no one but a real princess would be good enough to marry her son.

"A real princess," said the Queen, "is perfect in every way."

"A real princess is beautiful. A real princess is clever.

A real princess is sweet and very, very sensitive."

The prince travelled all over the world to try to find a real princess.

But there was something not quite right about every princess he met.

Some were too fat and some were too thin.

Some were too tall and some were too short.

Some were too ugly and some were too stupid.

Some were too greedy and none of them was really sensitive.

The prince went back to his castle. He was very sad.

"I will never find a real princess," he said. "I will never marry and have a family."

One dark night, there was a terrible storm. Thunder crashed, lightning flashed, and rain poured down from the sky.

Suddenly there was a loud knocking at the castle door. The prince's father, the King, went down to open it. A girl stood there. Water ran down her hair and clothes. It ran into the tops of her shoes and out through the toes.

"Please let me in," she said. "I am a princess."

"A real princess?" asked the King.

"A real princess," said the girl.

A real princess! The prince saw that the girl was beautiful and clever and sweet. He fell in love with her, and wanted to marry her.

But the Queen said to herself: "We shall soon find out if she is a real princess or not."

She hurried into the bedroom where royal guests slept. Then she took a small, dried pea — just one — and put it on the bed.

"Bring me a hundred mattresses," she told the maids. Then she called the King.

"I want a hundred mattresses on that bed," she told him. "Count them as they are put on."

"Oh, dear," said the King, "I never was any good at counting. I'll get the pageboys to help me. Count the mattresses as they are put on the bed," he told the boys. "Begin!"

And as each mattress was put on the bed, they counted. "One. Two. Three. Four."

"Five. Six. Seven. Eight. Nine. Ten." Then they stopped.

"I know what comes next," said the King. "Eleven!" And he looked very pleased with himself.

Then "Twelve," said the pages.

"Thirteen. Fourteen. Fifteen. Sixteen. Seventeen. Eighteen. Nineteen. Twenteen."

"No!" said the King. "Twenty. Even I know that."

Then "twenty-one to thirty," said the pages brightly. Then thirty-one to forty. Forty-one to fifty. Then sixty. Seventy. Eighty. Ninety to ninety-nine and . . . "a hundred!" said the page boys and King together, as the maids put on the last mattress.

"Good," said the King, "I knew we could do it." The Queen came back.

"Are you sure there are a hundred mattresses on the bed?" she asked.

"Yes," said the King. "We all counted."

"Good," said the Queen. "Tonight the girl will sleep on top of them, and tomorrow we will know if she is a real princess or not." The servants put a long ladder against the mattresses and the princess climbed up to the very top.

"Goodnight," said the Queen, and everyone left the room.

The next morning, the Queen came back into the bedroom.

"How did you sleep?" she asked. "Did you have a good night?"

"Oh, no," said the princess. "A dreadful night. I tossed and turned and couldn't sleep at all. There was something terribly hard in the bed. My whole body is black and blue with bruises. I don't think I ever had such a horrid night in all my life."

"Take away the mattresses," ordered the Queen, and she told the King to count them.

"Ninety-nine. Ninety-eight. Ninety-seven," counted the King, down to: "Ten. Nine. Eight. Seven. Six. Five. Four. Three. Two. One. Zero."

When the last mattress was taken away, the Queen showed everyone the dried pea.

"Only a real princess could be sensitive enough to feel one little pea through a hundred mattresses," said the Queen. She turned to the prince.

"You may ask her to be your wife," she said.

The prince and princess were married and lived happily ever after.

But wait! What did you say? No one, not even a real princess, could feel a pea under a hundred mattresses.

Well, you are right. She didn't. You see, the prince had a dog and a cat who saw the Queen put the pea on the bed. And when everyone left, the dog and cat told the princess, who slept very well all night, and knew exactly what to say to the Queen in the morning.

The prince and princess and their children looked after the dog and cat for the rest of their lives.

And the pea was put in the royal museum, where it can
be seen . . .

. . . to this very day.

by *Hans Andersen*, retold by *Milton Subotsky,* pictures by *Moo Movies*

Want to be a princess?

Want to be a princess?
Want to fall asleep
for a hundred years in a castle keep
or be snared by a witch
whose awful power
locks you inside a dark, dark tower
with a moat dank and deep
full of rats and eels?
Want to know how it feels
to be a dragon's tea,
or turned into a doe
or a dove, or a tree
by sneaky sorcerers
and other such cranks?

No thanks!

Pat Edwards

39

Medieval Castle

Cats, of course, don't mind whether they sleep in
a castle or a cottage . . .

Catnap

My cat sleeps
with her claws
clasped
and her long tail
curled.
My cat twitches
her tabby cheek
for the mice that
squeak

and the milk that
flows
by her pink, pink nose
in the purring warmth
of my cat's world.

Max Fatchen

. . . or even under the carpet!

Thank You, Dad for Everything.

Thank you for laying the carpet, dad,
Thank you for showing us how,
But what is that lump in the middle, dad?
And why is it saying mia-ow?

Doug MacLeod

43

Puss in boots

Once long ago there was a miller. When he became so old that he could no longer work, he divided his property among his three sons.

He left the mill to his oldest son,

and the donkey to his second son.

To his youngest son he left the cat, Puss.

The youngest son was very sad.

"My brothers can use the mill and the donkey to work together," he said. "But how can I ever make a living with just this cat?"

Now Puss was a clever cat and could understand what people said.

"Cheer up!" Puss said to the youngest son. "Have a pair of boots made for me so that I can run through the sharp brambles, and get me a sack with a cord. If you do this, you will never be unhappy again."

The miller's son was very surprised to hear the cat speak, but he did as Puss told him. He got Puss a sack with a strong cord and he had a fine pair of red leather boots made to the cat's size.

When Puss had learned to run in his new boots, he went to the bramble patch where many wild rabbits lived. Puss put some cabbage leaves and parsley and two carrots in the sack. Then he hid behind a tree and waited.

Soon a foolish young rabbit came along and hopped right into the sack. Puss quickly pulled tight the cord. He slung the sack over his shoulder and hurried to the King's castle.

Puss knocked at the door. Out came the King and his guards.

"How do you do, your Majesty," said Puss. "My master, the Marquis of Carabas, sends this rabbit to you."

"I have never heard of the Marquis of Carabas," exclaimed the King. "But I am very fond of fresh game, so I shall gladly accept this present."

The next day Puss went off to a wheat field. He filled the sack with golden grain. Then he hid in the high grass and made the sound of a partridge.

Soon a pair of foolish partridges heard the call and ran into the sack.

Puss pulled tight the cord on the sack and hurried to the King's castle.

"Good day, your Majesty," said Puss. "The Marquis of Carabas hopes that you will enjoy these birds at your dinner table."

"They are indeed fine birds," replied the King. He smacked his lips and called to his guards, "See that Cook prepares these at once!"

On the third morning Puss caught two large trout and brought them to the King, too.

"Here is another gift from my lord, the Marquis of Carabas," explained Puss. The King was very pleased.

He patted his round belly and said, "The Marquis must be a fine person to send me all these tasty treats."

As Puss was leaving, he heard the King's coachmen talking.

"The King has ordered that we ready his coach for a ride along the river today," said one.

"And he will be taking his daughter, the princess, with him," replied the other.

Puss ran all the way from the King's castle to the youngest son's house.

"Master," he cried, "today your fortune will be made! All you must do is go for a swim in the river. Leave the rest to me."

The miller's son did as Puss told him. He went to the river, took off his clothes, and jumped into the water. While he practised floating, Puss hid the young man's ragged clothes behind a rock.

No sooner had Puss done this than the King's coach drove up.

"Help, Help!" Puss yelled as he ran into the road.

"The Marquis of Carabas has been robbed!"

52

When the King heard this, he stuck his head out of the window.

"Stop the coach," he ordered. He recognised Puss and he remembered the many tasty gifts Puss's master had given to him.

"Your Majesty, someone has stolen my master's clothes," said Puss.

"Footman," the King ordered, "run back to the castle and fetch one of my best suits for the Marquis of Carabas."

The miller's son was very surprised.

"Who is the Marquis of Carabas?" he whispered to Puss.

"I have told the King that you are the Marquis," Puss whispered in reply.

The miller's son dressed in the rich suit of clothes and indeed, he looked as splendid as any Marquis.

"Now you must thank the King," said Puss. "Leave the rest to me and your fortune will soon be made."

The miller's son thanked the King politely for the new clothes.

"You are most welcome," replied the King. "Now would you please join us for a ride in the coach." The miller's son sat next to the Princess, who was happy to see such a handsome young man.

Puss ran ahead till he came to a field where some haymakers were working.

"Haymakers!" called Puss in a fierce voice. "When the King drives past and asks to whom this field belongs, you must reply, 'To the Marquis of Carabas.' If you don't, I shall chop you fine as mincemeat."

Soon the King passed by in his coach.

"To whom does this fine hayfield belong?" he asked.

"To our lord, the Marquis of Carabas," replied the haymakers, for they had been greatly frightened by Puss.

Then Puss ran on till he came to a field where some reapers were working.

"Reapers!" called Puss in an even fiercer voice than before. "When the King drives past and asks to whom this field belongs, you must reply, 'To the Marquis of Carabas.' If you don't, I shall chop you fine as mincemeat!"

Soon the King passed by in his coach.

"To whom does this fine field of grain belong?" he asked.

"To our lord, the Marquis of Carabas," replied the reapers, for they too had been greatly frightened by Puss.

"You have very fine land," the King said to the miller's son.

The young man saw what Puss was up to and said nothing. But he smiled at the Princess and she smiled back at him.

Puss ran as hard as his boots could carry him till he came to a great castle.

The castle belonged to a wicked old Giant. The Giant owned all the lands the King had just passed by, and for years he had forced the haymakers and reapers to work for him.

Puss had heard that the Giant also possessed the powers of a magician.

"What do you want?" the Giant roared when he saw it was only a cat who had disturbed him.

"I could not pass this way," Puss replied, "without paying respect to the most famous of magicians."

This greatly pleased the Giant, who let Puss into his hall.

"Is it really true that you can change yourself into a lion or an elephant or anything you choose?" asked Puss.

"Oh, yes, I can change into many animals," grinned the Giant.

BOOM! A loud clap of thunder echoed through the castle and there stood an elephant.

"Amazing!" exclaimed Puss, who stood out of the way of the swinging trunk. Suddenly the elephant roared and there stood a lion.

"How fantastic!" cried Puss, though he was very much afraid. "It must be easy for you to turn into something large. But can you also turn into something small?"

"Yes!" roared the lion, and in an instant a little mouse scurried across the floor. That was just what Puss had been waiting for. With one pounce he caught the mouse and ate it up. And that was the end of the wicked old Giant.

By and by the King's coach arrived at the Giant's castle.

"Welcome to the castle of the Marquis of Carabas," Puss announced with a bow.

"Does this beautiful castle belong to you, too, my lord Marquis?" asked the King. He was greatly impressed.

Puss brought them all to the dining hall. There a great feast had been prepared by the servants, who were much happier obeying Puss than the wicked Giant.

The King was very pleased with the handsome young Marquis and his castle and all his lands. "You may ask my daughter to marry you, since you both seem so fond of each other."

The Princess agreed, and they had the wedding that very afternoon.

There was a great celebration that lasted long into the night. Puss in his red leather boots led all the dances.

61

"Thank you for all your help," the miller's son told
Puss, when the merriment was finally over.
  Next day he had a special throne made for Puss.
And they all lived happily ever after.

Italian folktale, retold and illustrated
by Paul Galdone

Sacks of words

Glossary

banquet (*p. 41*)
a special dinner for many people

battlements (*p. 40*)
a low wall around the roof of a castle or fort, with spaces to shoot through

brambles (*p. 17*)
thorny, prickly bushes

cobbler (*p. 4*)
someone who makes and mends shoes

crank (*p. 39*)
someone with strange or odd ideas

dank (*p. 39*)
unpleasantly wet and cold

doe (*p. 39*)
female deer

game (*p. 49*)
the meat of wild animals, such as rabbits

loyalty (*p. 40*)
to be true to someone or something, so that they trust you

keep (*p. 39*)
the great tower of a castle where people live

Glossary continues on page 64

Marquis (*p. 49*)
an important person like a duke or lord

merriment (*p. 62*)
laughter and enjoyment

miller (*p. 45*)
person who works a mill that produces flour

soda (*p. 40*)
a chemical mixture that is used in making soap

sorcerer (*p. 39*)
someone who does things by using bad magic

mutton (*p. 40*)
the meat that comes from a sheep

reapers (*p. 56*)
people who cut corn, wheat etc.

sensitive (*p. 29*)
easily hurt or upset

snared (*p. 39*)
caught and trapped

sourpuss (*p. 44*)
a person who always complains

spills (*p. 41*)
food and drink that spilt onto the floor

steward (*p. 41*)
the head servant